Monster Poems

Brian Moses lives in a small Sussex village with his wife and two daughters. He travels the UK presenting his poetry and percussion shows in schools and libraries. He has produced a monstrous pile of poetry for Macmillan Children's Books, is a firm believer in the existence of the Loch Ness Monster, and still checks under the bed before he goes to sleep at night. Well, doesn't everyone?

Axel Scheffler spent a relatively monster-free childhood in Hamburg, Germany, checking frequently under his bed. He came to the UK in 1982 and has been illustrating books ever since. In 1999 he created the monstrously successful *The Gruffalo* with Julia Donaldson.

Monster Poems

Chosen by
Brian Moses

Illustrated by Axel Scheffler

MACMILLAN CHILDREN'S BOOKS

For the children in BMC (Brian Moses' Class), Kevin, James, Josh, Luke, Elliot,
Alex, Daniel, Adam, Callum, Ben B, Jordan, Carl, Craig, Fraser, Lewis, Tyler,
Ben R, Hollie, Eleanor, Chloe, Larissa, Giorgia, May, Madeleine, Bethany,
Charlotte, Emilia, Izzy, Nikita, Ruby-Lou and Sydney, and for their teacher,
Sarah Williams, at Telscombe Cliffs Community School, East Sussex

First published 2005 by Macmillan Children's Books
a division of Macmillan Publishers Limited
20 New Wharf Road, London N1 9RR
Basingstoke and Oxford
www.panmacmillan.com

Associated companies throughout the world

ISBN 0 330 42048 8

3 5 7 9 8 6 4

A CIP catalogue record for this book is available from
the British Library.

Printed and bound in Great Britain by Mackays of Chatham plc, Kent

Contents

Now I'm Not a Little Kid

I can't believe I used to think
there were such things as beasts
that prowled with blood-red, killer's eyes
the forests of our sleep,
nor monsters formed from Devil's touch
or by a witch's spell,
nor creatures foul and hideous
that found their way from Hell.
There's nothing much that scares me now,
I think I'm pretty tough
and though I look beneath my bed,
it's just to check for dust.

Trevor Parsons

Detecting Monsters

Here are some questions
to ask yourself if you suspect
that your home conceals monsters.

Are there any beds?

Monsters sleep under beds –
any beds – but don't worry unduly
unless yours is a four-poster!

Are there any cupboards?

Monsters relax in cupboards.
Not kitchen or airing cupboards –
too cramped and small –

but tall, cobwebby cupboards
especially if they're under stairs
or down dark, echoey corridors.

Is there a cellar?

Monsters hold parties in cellars.
And if it's always locked . . .
well I'd be very suspicious but . . .

if you've got an attic ...

now you're talking –
you're sure to have monsters!

What to do if your home has monsters.

Creep about as quietly as you can
and hope the monsters
never discover *their* home conceals you!

Philip Waddell

Monster Love

Monsters, when wooing, must always take care
That their gestures of love serve to soothe and not scare,
For their tenderest whisper may sound like a roar,
And their gentle caresses all end in a claw.

Julia Rawlinson

The Monsters

Some are ugly,
Some are tall,
Some are scary,
Some are small.
Some are difficult to see.
And some are in my family.

Emma Hjeltnes

The Monster That Ate the Universe

I began with a pancake
But why stop there?
So I ate the spoon
And the table and chair
I ate all the cutlery
I ate the cheese grater
The cooker, the microwave
The refrigerator

I wolfed down the kitchen
The dining room too.
I slurped up the bathroom
including the loo
I chewed up the house
I gulped it all down
I ate the whole street.
Then I swallowed the town

I devoured the country.
Then what do you think?
I drank the ocean
(I needed a drink)
Then the Earth I consumed
The planets, the sun
I was still feeling peckish
And having such fun

So I gorged on the galaxy
Then the galaxy next door
I was still feeling hungry
So I gobbled up more
I dined on them all
As the prophets all feared
Then I swallowed myself
And (burp!) disappeared

In the silence that followed
A little bird sang
Then nothing. Just silence.
And a very big Bang!

Roger Stevens

Monster Crazy

Everyone here has gone Monster Crazy,
even those who are normally lazy,
binoculars raised, though the view may be hazy,
everyone here has gone Monster Crazy.

So come on, Nessie, give us a wave,
don't stay hidden in your underwater cave.
You're the talk of the town, the darling of the press,
it wouldn't be summer without you in Loch Ness.

Just come on up and prove that you're there,
sometime or other you must surface for air,
somebody's camera will photograph you,
proving, at last, if you're one hump or two!

Everyone here has gone Monster Crazy,
even those who are normally lazy,
binoculars raised, though the view may be hazy,
everyone here has gone Monster Crazy.

Just waggle your flipper or flip your tail,
make some fisherman's face turn pale
as you lift your head to look at the view,
there are hundreds waiting to interview you.

Just one word, Nessie, go on be a pet,
can't you stop playing hard to get?
You could be on TV, you'd have lots of money,
American tourists all calling you 'Honey!'

Everyone here has gone Monster Crazy,
even those who are normally lazy,
binoculars raised, though the view may be hazy,
everyone here has gone Monster Crazy.

Brian Moses

Yeti

I claim with confidence, I've met
Most creatures in the alphabet.
I've hunted them with noose or net,
From aardvark, ape and avocet,
Through musk-ox, moose and marmoset,
To xiphias and zebra, yet
It is to my intense regret
I haven't seen a Yeti ... yet.

I've trekked by mule with my machete,
Getting chilly, mucky, sweaty,
And, though you may call it petty,
Still I've never found a Yeti.

I've searched regions dry and wet.
I've scoured the plateau of Tibet.
I've studied Yeti etiquette,
Seen things I think a Yeti's ate,
And though I'm not the sort to fret,
I'm really getting quite upset
That I've not seen or smelt or met
Or found or caught a Yeti . . . yet!

Paul Bright

Scary Movies for Monsters

When monsters go to the movies
To try to get a scare,
What really makes them tremble
Is not: *The Mummy's Stare!*

The Zombie's Kiss! or *Bat Craze!*
Or *Shrieking Ghouls That Roam!*
These movies make them chuckle -
It makes them feel at home.

What really makes them shudder
And turns their dark hair white -
The classic horror movie!
The 100-Watt Night Light!

Or *Kids with Giant Flashlights!*
It makes them quake with dread,
Or *Angry Mobs with Torches!*
Or *Floodlights 'Neath the Bed!*

It makes them spill their popcorn,
It gives them nasty frights,
And when the movie's over,
There's scary theatre lights.

They leave the movies shaken,
And very soon they crave,
A place a lot more soothing -
Some haunted bat-filled cave!

Robert Scotellaro

The Museum of Mythical Beasts

Go right in, past a beam of light
that shoots from a Cyclops' eye,
then put on armour and pick up a sword,
test how much of a hero you are:
Only the bravest and best may steal the gold
from a griffin's nest.

Then try to resist a mermaid's song.
How long will you stay before you're forced
to block your ears and turn away?

Now braver souls have tangled with trolls,
they'll carry you off to be their slave.
Careful, don't trip, just a pile of old bones,
previous visitors, I suppose!

A date with Medusa! What a surprise!
Keep your head and don't look in her eyes.
Move forward once more till you reach a door.
The Minotaur is next on our list,
a horrible task, you'd be well advised
to go prepared when you visit his lair.

That terrible smell is the Gorgon of death;
run past, run fast, don't waste any time
in escaping the blast of its breath.

Beware the Roc that will snatch you away
as a plaything for one of her young
or the goblins already hung over their pans
or the two-headed ogre who can't decide
which mouth he should slide you in!

And now you head for the final test,
a dragon, so deadly, so dreadful, so strong.
Don't weaken at all when you hear her ROAR
as you score more points with Saint George.

Then at the exit, don't forget
to collect your certificate,
dated and signed to say you survived
the museum of mythical beasts.

Brian Moses

The Marrog

My desk's at the back of the class
  And nobody, nobody knows
    I'm a Marrog from Mars
With a body of brass
  And seventeen fingers and toes.

Wouldn't they shriek if they knew
  I've three eyes at the back of my head
    And my hair is bright purple
My nose is deep blue
  And my teeth are half-yellow, half-red.

My five arms are silver, and spiked
  With knives on them sharper than spears.
I could go back right now, if I liked -
  And return in a million light-years.

I could gobble them all,
For I'm seven foot tall
  And I'm breathing green flames from my ears.

Wouldn't they yell if they knew,
  If they guessed that a Marrog was here?
Ha-ha, they haven't a clue –
  Or wouldn't they tremble with fear!
'Look, look, a Marrog'
  They'd all scream - and SMACK
The blackboard would fall and the ceiling would crack
  And teacher would faint, I suppose.
But I grin to myself, sitting right at the back
  And nobody, nobody knows.

R. C. Scriven

The Little Ogre

It's hard to be an ogre
when you've only just been born.
It's hard to snarl and gnash your teeth
when you've no teeth at all.

It's hard to menace with intent,
to throw your weight around.
It's hard to roar and howl and shout,
to stomp and shake the ground.

It's hard to stare and glare
until your victim's mesmerized
or turned to stone, or dies of fright,
when you've bright blue baby eyes.

You can manage a good dribble,
you can do that any time,
but it's runny, weak and milky
not a lovely gooey slime.

You crawl in for the kill,
you lunge to strike the fatal blow
and manage (more or less)
to suck an ankle or toe.

Life's tough for little ogres.
Humans laugh when you're so small.
Humans don't take little ogres
seriously at all.

Don't despair, your turn will come.
You'll find they soon stop crowing
When they see you grow and keep on

growing, growing, growing, growing!

Patricia Leighton

Ten Mighty Monsters

Ten mighty monsters swinging on a vine
One smashed into a tree, then there were nine.

Nine mighty monsters on a river in full spate
One tipped over in the rapids, then there were eight.

Eight mighty monsters climbing up a cliff in Devon
One fell in the sea below, then there were seven.

Seven mighty monsters building shelters using sticks
One stuck in a snowdrift, then there were six.

Six mighty monsters taking speedboats for a drive
One hit the harbour wall, then there were five.

Five mighty monsters flying off to Ecuador
One lost its passport, then there were four.

Four mighty monsters surfing in Torquay
One was swept out by a wave, then there were three.

Three mighty monsters learning to lasso
One was dragged off by a steer, then there were two.

Two mighty monsters weightlifting a ton
One went through the floorboards, then there was one.

One mighty monster filming with James Bond
Set off an explosion and ran off with a blonde.

Penny Kent

Morning Monster

The door slowly creaked open
Attempting to focus its bloodshot eyes
Its hair a mass of tangled knots
It shuffled down the hallway
Hunched over
Hands about level with its knees
A low grunt emitted from somewhere
Within its grey stubbled face.
I spoke only two words to it,
'Morning, Dad', I said.

Donald Nelson

The Sliver-slurk

Down beneath the frogspawn,
Down beneath the reeds,
Down beneath the river's shimmer,
Down beneath the weeds,
Down in dirty darkness,
Down in muddy murk
Down amongst the sludgy shadows
Lives the Sliver-slurk;

Lives the Sliver-slurk
And the Sliver-slurk's a thing
With a gnawing kind of nibble
And a clammy kind of cling,
With a row of warts on top
And a row of warts beneath
And a horrid way of bubbling through
Its green and stumpy teeth;

With its green and stumpy teeth,
Oh, the Sliver-slurk's a beast
That you'd never find invited
To a party or a feast -
It would terrify the guests,
Make them shake and shout and scream,
Crying: 'Save us from this loathsomeness,
This monster from a dream!'

It's a monster from a dream,
Haunting waters grey and grim,
So be careful when you paddle
Or go happily to swim:
It is down there, it is waiting,
It's a nasty piece of work
And you might just put your foot upon
The slimy Sliver-slurk.

Richard Edwards

Mirror Monster

Only I see stone
in the deep of sparkling eyes,
admiring my face.

Only I see snakes
corkscrew in the twisted curls
of my fiery hair

Only I see fur
on my pale and moonlit skin
as I pull back sleeves.

Only I see hooves
when I take off my slippers,
get ready for bed.

Only I see blood
drip from the teeth of a smile
tasting of terror.

Only the mirror
shows me the monster I am –
and keeps my secret.

Celia Gentles

I Wonder Why

So many people frown at me,
I often wonder why.
But I don't mind.
I just smile back,
and wink my middle eye.

Barry Buckingham

All the Trappings

Said The Mummy, 'I'm starting to find
That this job is a bit of a bind.
    Though I'm white as a sheet
    And feel dead on my feet
I just don't get the chance to *unwind*!'

Graham Denton

The Loch Ness Monster's School Report

Literacy   Writing is poor. His ink tends to run.

Numeracy Knows how many humps make five.

ICT   Must learn not to get his mouse waterlogged,
and overcome his fear of the Internet.

History   Has an excellent understanding of dinosaurs.

Art   Should extend his range. He has painted
twenty pictures this year, all called
'View from a Lake'.

RE   Must try not to bellow during hymn
practice.

Science   Demonstrates a good knowledge of fish,
amphibians and water birds –
and knows some interesting recipes for them.

PE   Room for improvement in running and
jumping, but he excels at swimming.

Conduct   A polite student, but rather shy.
He would make more friends if he didn't
insist on playing hide-and-seek.

Alison Chisholm

Out of Work Gremlin

I'm a gremlin who's out of work.
I'm a gremlin with nothing to do.
I would like to come to your house
And fill all your sneakers with glue.

The mischief I'd bring you is charming.
If you're bored you will love me around.
I'll stay 'neath your bed when it's night time,
And I'll make just a small eerie sound.

I'm a gremlin who's out of work.
I can cut little holes in your pants.
I can smear gooey jam on your T-shirt
And sprinkle your pizza with ants.

I can boil all your toys in green mustard -
Put frogs in your bed sheets at night.
I can tie, in square knots, your shoelaces.
And solder your lunch box up tight.

I can drill tiny holes in your soup bowl.
I can put itchy things in your socks.
I can melt all your crayons and felt tips
And freeze all the hands of your clocks

So if you are seeking some mischief,
Some small, little devilish perk.
Just call, and I'll hurry on over.
I'm a gremlin who's out of work.

Robert Scotellaro

The Worst Monster

The worst monster in the world lives at the bottom of my garden.
She lives in the bushes just past the apple tree
And never comes out unless she's wearing her frock of old shadows
Patched with bits of night.
Plus, a little bright ribbon in her hair.
I can always see her ribbon, like eyes, really, shining in the dark.
'You can't be scared of a monster who wears a ribbon,'
    people laugh.
'Oh, can't you!' I say.
'You should be here when she creeps into the house and lies in wait
    on the stairs.
Or when she sidles into my room and hides under the bed.
I bet you'd be scared!'
I can handle that.
Well, most of the time, I can, but maybe not at midnight when the
    church clock
Chimes twelve times,
Calling out witches and wizards, floaty ghosts and hungry monsters
Who tap you on the shoulder and breathe down the back of your neck.

Yet, none of them are as scary as my monster,
Who wears a ribbon in her hair and hides at the bottom of the garden,
Waiting to get me.
The worst time, the scariest time,
Is not when she's hiding in the bushes just past the apple tree.
It's when she stands up and, without taking one foot off the ground,
Catches the moon in her dark mouth and swallows it!
Then, I can't see anything,
Not even her ribbon,
And I am more afraid than ever.

Gwen Grant

Fancy a Game?

Here's my Monster footy team:

Keeper: King Kong - he's useless, but he does block the whole goal.

Defenders:
Cyclops - always keeps his eye on the ball;
Pegasus - plays centaur half;
Werewolf - excellent at long loud offside calls;
Phoenix - good in the air (recently made a great comeback too).

Midfield:
Godzilla - provides a bit of bite in the tackle;
Big Foot - free-kick specialist;
Dragon - very pacy (burns around the pitch);
Roc - good on the wing.

Attack:
Cerberus - has two sweet left feet;
Medusa - defenders are petrified when she's on form.

Fancy a game?

Andy Seed

Winter Fiends

The wild wind turns trees into demons -
each branch whips its bare bony claw.

The purple sea writhes like a serpent,
Devours the beach with a roar.

My dressing gown shivers - a phantom
that shadows the back of the door.

Our lonely house howls like a werewolf -
each window a wide gaping jaw.

Celia Gentles

My Sister's a Monster

My sister's a monster -
It's true.
I know, because I've seen her change
From sugar and spice and oh-so-nice to

A raving, ranting beast
With bulging eyes
And long, wild hair;
I've even seen two horns appear
Out of her head, I swear.

Of course,
No one believes me when I tell them.
They think I'm just exaggerating,
Fabricating;
But that's because they never see
My sister's transformation
From human being into this *thing*.
Oh no. She keeps that certain revelation
Just for me.

You wait. One day soon
My sister will forget herself
In front of all our friends and family:
Her eyes will bulge
And two sharp horns will grow -
Then everyone will know
That my sister's a monster.

Gillian Floyd

The Banshee Choir Practice

Come along, ladies, take a deep breath
And sing me a song of doom and death.

Make the audience quake and quail
With your hideous howls and woeful wails.

Those screechy notes are really thrilling
But get that trilling more spine-chilling.

And please make an effort to sing off-key,
I'm looking for wild disharmony.

Drown out the rhythm and the musical beat
With a chorus of shrill blood-curdling shrieks.

Now let's have a real cacophony:
On my count - one, two and THREE ...

Cynthia Rider

The Woebegone and the Woebetide

O woebetide you if upon
Your bed you find a Woebegone;
And woebetide you if beside
That beast there sits a Woebetide.

These beasts are often found in pairs,
There is no friendship quite like theirs;
They love each other, but it's true
They do not care for me or you.

So if by chance you come upon
The beast they call the Woebegone,
Be off! Or you'll end up inside
His only friend, the Woebetide.

(And likewise you should run and hide
If you should see a Woebetide –
Or else you might end up upon
The menu of the Woebegone.)

Colin West

Lonely Hearts Club

Is your skin all cold and slimy?
Do you sport a toothless grin?
Are your toenails black and grimy?
Is your hairline wearing thin?
Do your armpits smell all musty?
Does your nose drip purple snot?
Are your piggy eyes all crusty?
Do you grunt and belch a lot?
Is your belly like a jelly?
Do your ears ooze waxy gunk?
Is your underwear all smelly?
Is your house crammed full of junk?

If so and you are female
And you live a lonely life
You're just like me, so give us a ring
I'm looking for a wife.

Richard Caley

The Ice Dragons

They tell of Polar dragons
Who breathe frost instead of fire,
With icicles nine along their backs,
Each one a glassy spire.
In the eerie light
Of that endless white
Where bleak winds always blow,
They make their homes
Neath icy domes
In everlasting snow.
And when these dragons gather
(This is the tale that's told)
They stand in an Arctic Circle,
They breathe
And the world grows cold.

Eric Finney

Beautician and the Beast

Good morning, sir. What will it be today?
A wedding makeover. How lovely!
Will sir be requiring sharpening of the claws?
French manicure?
Descaling and exfoliation?
Waxing of the ears and head massage?
Full facial? Nose-hair tinting?
Stinkatherapy for relaxation?
The whole package?

Will sir's fiancée
Be paying us a visit?
Yes, I understand
And I can guarantee
This time *you'll* be
The Beast of the Ball,
All ready
To live happily ever after!

Sue Cowling

Don't Ever Ogle an Ogre

Don't ever ogle an ogre
Or look a Cyclops in the eye.
Don't ever phone up a phantom.
Let the bogeyman boogie on by.

Don't shake the hand of a banshee
Or offer a hellhound a bone.
Don't go for a stroll with a terrible troll.
They are beasts who are best left alone.

Don't give your help to a kelpie
Or hector a spectre. Beware!
Don't ever get close to a gorgon.
She'll attack without turning a hair.

Don't drag a dragon out shopping
Or treat a fiend as your friend.
Don't ever say Hi to a harpy
Or you could meet a horrible end.

For the truth of the matter is simple.
Most monsters are evil and vile.
They will beat you, defeat you, and probably eat you,
And only then will they smile!

Rosie Kent

The Creak

In
the
attic
lives a
Creak. Does
anyone know
What Creaks eat?
Sometimes he hides
Up the stairs,
With Squeak and Growl,
Who both live there.
Their friend Tip Taps
A proper pain,
Jabbing at the
window frame.
On windy nights
Whoosh comes in too.
He likes the vent
Behind the loo.
No one wants

Whoosh in the attic.
Creak and Squeak,
Make such a racket.
Tip Tap bangs
To be let in,
But Growl
creates
The biggest din.
Soon old Whoosh is sulking hard.
Kicking bins around the yard,
Tearing leaves off, clanking gates,
Screeching and howling in pipes and grates.
In the attic lives a Creak,
And on the stairs
Live Growl and Squeak.
Tip Tap and Whoosh
Fought all this week,
And I just want a bit of peace!

Sue Hardy Dawson

53

Song of the Lonely Monster

So many oceans deep,
So many mountains high,
So many slopes so steep,
So many tears to cry.

So many chasms wide,
So many ice-caps cold,
So many hurts inside,
So many griefs to hold.

So many deserts vast,
So many forests drear,
So many ages past,
So many more to scare.

So many drifts of snow,
So many stars above,
So many miles to go
And never a friend to love.

John Mole

The Creatures That Crouch
Beneath My Bed

(after a song by John Dowie)

Well,
beasts beneath my bed
are worse than
hobgoblins from hell
and
hobgoblins from hell
are worse than
fire-breathing fiends
and
fire-breathing fiends
are worse than
ghostly, ghastly ghouls
and
ghostly, ghastly ghouls
are worse than
deadly dinosaurs
and
deadly dinosaurs
are worse than
teachers in our school

and
teachers in our school
are worst than
beasts beneath my bed.

Nick Toczek

Monsters Lurk
Where You Least Expect

The Spotted Weeblebeebleslop
has a pink and pointed nose
it scuttles round your living room
on its ten thousand toes
snuffling up small scraps of fluff
from underneath the door
with its sticky-snaky tongue
slurping round the floor
be careful you're not slobbered on
by this revolting creature
though happily it only measures
half a millimetre.

You'll find the Flying Snotterdroop
on your bedroom curtain
leaving long and slimy tracks
of this you can be certain
its stink and mess will fill your room
until it drives you mad
the Snideydrip and the Wongle Worm
are nearly just as bad
the only way to rid yourself
of these revolting pests
is to scare them out with sweaty socks
and Grandma's unwashed vests.

The Double-headed Fangle Fish
floats in with the breeze
it'll swim right up your nostrils
and make you cough and sneeze
worse than that it sinks its teeth
into your arm or leg
squeezes, squirms, jiggles, jumps
proceeds to lay an egg
watch out for the Horror Hopper
leaping on your cat
and beware the Skunkfaced Snoot
and the Purple Burple Bat.

59

Yes, all these monsters live their lives
underneath your roof
The Central Eating Pimple Fly
with its one and only tooth
The Giant See-through Blunder Bug
the microscopic Squail
with its fifteen piggy eyes
and its stinging tail
you might not see them all the time
not each and every day
but, believe me, they're all there
and they intend to stay.

David Harmer

King Kong's Car Boot Sale

1 biplane (slightly damaged),
1 TV aerial from Empire State Building (needs attention),
6 photos of New York,
12,000 banana skins,
4 copies of *Oversized Ape Monthly* (mint condition),
1 pair underpants (XXXXXXXXL)

Andy Seed

Cerberus, the Dog

Cerberus is not a pet I would get.
Nor is it one I would let
Anywhere near me.
It's scary and hairy:
A three-headed hound,
Each head
The size of a football,
Each mouth
Reeking of decay.
Its six eyes
Red as burst tomatoes.
Its three tails
Coiling and hissing behind it.
If it broke free
One head would swallow the moon,
One head would swallow the sun,
One head would swallow the stars.
No, Cerberus is not
The kind of pet
I would get.

Brian Patten

The New School Bus Driver

His ears point up
His hair sticks out
His neck is seven feet about
If he turns round I'm going to shout
Please keep him facing forwards

His back is a peculiar shape
It's all hunched up, just like an ape
Until I've worked out my escape
Please keep him facing forwards

His spiky fingers grip the wheel
They're grey and shiny, just like steel
My blood's beginning to congeal
Please keep him facing forwards

I see reflected in the dash
Red pointy eyes that flare and flash
Please God, I don't care if we crash
Please keep him facing forwards

He turns
I scream
His mouth drools pus
I wouldn't normally make a fuss
But I'm the last one on the bus
Please keep him facing . . . . arrrrrgh!

Andrea Shavick

The Yaffling Yahoo

(a do-it-yourself Space Beast)

The Yaffling Yahoo
is made of blue glue,
    but when she feels mean
    she turns a bright . . . .

She shrinks herself small
when dry rain starts to fall.
    She's an ugly disgrace
    with those splumps on her . . . .

She enjoys a long drink
from a tank of pink ink.
    Then will sprint down the street
    on her twelve pairs of . . . .

When her back gets an itch
then her nose starts to twitch.
    She is skyscraper tall
    yet as round as a . . . .

The Yaffling Yahoo
just hasn't a clue.
　　She continues to chase
　　through the dark depths of.......

Wes Magee

Sky-Dragon

I am Sky-Dragon,
Lord of the thunder,
When I bellow and roar
Clouds tear asunder.

When I raise my claw,
The pouring rain
Cascades from the sky
Flooding valley and plain.

When I lash my tail,
The howling gales
Snap the masts of ships
And shred their sails.

When I breathe my fire
Zigzag stripes
Flash through the air
As the lightning strikes.

I am Sky-Dragon,
When you hear me roar,
Fasten your windows
And bolt the door.

John Foster

Monster Menu

Soup
Staple soup seasoned to taste
With iron filings and nuclear waste

Hors d'oeuvres
Candied ants in diesel dips
Served with fried computer chips

Entrée
Poached roach sautéed in slime
or
Legs of lizard stewed in grime

Dessert
Mouse mousse jubilee
Termite tea (caffeine-free)

Douglas Florian

The Up-the-Dark-Alley, Under-the-Bouncy-Bed, Behind-the-Cupboard-Door Monsters

A cloudy, moonless evening,
street lights not working,
street lights not working,
street lights not working,
on a cloudy, moonless evening
and the street lights not working

> *hoo-hoo here he comes*
> *the Up-the-Dark-Alley Monster*
> *with his black cape, his greased-back hair*
> *and his eyes as red as ketchup.*

A darkly midnight bedroom,
the bedside light out,
the bedside light out,
the bedside light out,
in a darkly midnight bedroom
and the bedside light out

hoo-hoo here he comes
the Under-the-Bouncy-Bed Monster
with paisley-pattern pyjamas, his teddy bear slippers
and with a spring in his step.

A silent, empty hallway,
the cupboard door shut,
the cupboard door shut,
the cupboard door shut,
and the hallway silent, empty
and the cupboard door shut

hoo-hoo here he comes
the Behind-the-Cupboard-Door Monster
with his loose handle, his scratched paint
and with his many coats hanging from his teeth.

Yes, it's the
Up-the-Dark-Alley,
Under-the-Bouncy-Bed,
Behind-the-Cupboard-Door
Monsters

and they're looking for some fun!!!

John Rice

Kraken

One thousand years he's lurked now
beneath Atlantic waves;
his tentacles coil gently
round careless sailors' graves.
He sinks and whirlpools open
that swallow man or beast;
he swims - a tidal wave begins
engulfing west and east.

He's heavier than a hurricane,
as tall as redwood trees;
his arms can grip the biggest ships
that sail the seven seas.
His eyeball is like Jupiter
and when he blows out spray
it covers earth and moon and sun
for three weeks and a day.

So should you ever hoist your sails
near transatlantic deeps,
though all seems calm, remember
the restless Kraken sleeps.
Don't set your sails too boldly
in transatlantic deeps;
though all is calm, remember,
the Kraken merely sleeps . . .

Judith Nicholls

Finding a Dragon's Lair

The way to find a dragon's lair
is down the road that goes nowhere,
over the bridge of Curse-And-Swear
on the river of Deep Despair.

Take the track to Give-You-A-Scare
across the marsh of Say-A-Prayer,
over the peak of Past Repair
and down the cliff of Do Beware.

Through the valley of If-You-Dare
you'll find the town of Don't-Go-There
where folk won't speak but stand and stare
and nobody will be Lord Mayor.

Beyond lies land that's parched and bare,
a dried-up lake named None-To-Spare,
a rock that's known as Life's Unfair
and hills they call No-Longer-Care.

It's hard to breathe the dreadful air
and in the sun's relentless glare
the heat becomes too much to bear.
You'll not be going anywhere.

You're weak and dazed but just aware
of something moving over there
approaching to inspect its snare.
And then you smell the dragon's lair.

Nick Toczek

Search for a Monstar

A long and nervous winding queue
with everyone wondering how they'll do.
The mummy's already quite wound up,
Mr Jekyll sips from a foaming cup.

Rehearsing phantoms moan and whine,
While quiet spectres gloat and shine.
The gryphons suddenly flap their wings.
Who's going to be the first to sing?

A voice calls from the green baize door,
Here's one we haven't heard before.
The judge, a ghoul, calls the first act.
His voice is harsh and that's a fact.

Werewolf sings 'been working like a dog',
Banshees wail for a lonely bog.
Vampire enters, bows, finds a key
Hisses 'Save your kisses for me'.

The skeleton really struts his stuff
The troll sings 'Three Billy Goats Gruff'.
The zombie sings 'I Will Survive'!
Sadly he looks more dead than alive.

Big Bad Wolf howls 'The Lady in Red'.
But foams at the mouth and loses his head.
The witch duets with an ugly gnome.
Minotaur roars 'Show Me the Way Home'.

Till finally, when all's said and sung
Sadly, we find no one has won.
They fought and chased each other away
but we'll audition another day.

And now we've done all we can do,
Listen out for a noise near you!
Watch out! Shut the window! Lock your cars!
Deep in the shadow lurk the next Monstars!

Simon Virgo

The Motorway Monster

The motorway monster makes you sick
It's always got to get somewhere quick
It comes out of nowhere
It's hot on your trail
It flashes its eyes
And bites at your tail.

The motorway monster is shiny and sleek
But its wits are poor and its brain is weak
Just slip to the side
It will rush out of sight
Perhaps later you'll see it
... By a flashing blue light!

Simon Virgo

Monster Sale!!

'MONSTER SALE!!' the advert said.
I'm telling you – it LIED.
There was junk galore
In the Super Store . . .
But not ONE monster inside.

Clare Bevan

Charm for Sweet Dreams

May the Ghost
   lie in its grave.
May the Vampire
   see the light.
May the Witch
   keep to her cave,
and the Spectre
   melt from sight.

May the Wraith
   stay in the wood.
May the Banshee
   give no fright.
May the Ghoul
   be gone for good,
and the Zombie
   haste its flight.

May the Troll
  no more be seen.
May the Werewolf
  lose its bite.
May all Spooks
  and Children Green
fade for ever
  in
    the
      night . . .

Wes Magee

I'm the Best Monster Around

My teacher yells and screams at me
Did you put glue in Sally's hair?
I smile and say
Why yes of course, do you see any other monsters here?

My mum looks crazed as she says
Did you spill the cream on the dining-room chair?
I grin evilly and say
Why yes of course, do you see any other monsters here?

My nanny stomps her foot at me
Did you rip apart your sister's teddy bear?
I wrinkle my nose and say
Of course, do you see any other monsters here?

Being a monster is hard enough
When you live in this tiny town
But hey at least I can say
I'm the best monster around!

Katherine Brandt

Monster Boast

He's big as a gorilla
but he fits into my hand,
his skin is made of metal
and his blood is made of sand.

He can breathe underwater
though he'd rather breathe air
and he grants me special wishes
which he keeps in his hair.

He doesn't like the darkness
even though he CAN see
and he doesn't like broccoli
(just like me).

He can walk on the ceiling
AND he can fly,
he's got a door in his stomach
that serves gognacious pie.

It's him that you should blame for
eating chocolates off the tree
and hiding all the wrappers
under the settee.

He isn't being naughty -
it's just the way he's made:
he ONLY eats chocolate
and he drinks lemonade.

You'd like to meet my monster?
I'm afraid he's very shy.
He gets invisibility
when grown-ups pass by.

I'll show you his tooth marks, though,
here, on my bed,
the ones that look like felt-tip, yes,
his teeth are blue and red.

Oh, and he's got antlers
AND he's magnetic . . .
his hands are made of comic books
AND . . . oh, forget it!

Ros Barber

A selected list of titles available from Macmillan Children's Books

The prices shown below are correct at the time of going to press. However, Macmillan Publishers reserves the right to show new retail prices on covers which may differ from those previously advertised.

Poems of Childhood   0 330 41567 0   £4.99
A celebration of childhood in verse, edited by Brian Moses

Dinos, Dodos and Other Dead Things 0 330 41564 6   £3.99
Poems Chosen by Brian Moses

Taking out the Tigers   0 330 41797 5   £3.99
Brian Moses

Beware of the Dinner Lady   0 330 43640 6   £3.99
School Poems Chosen by Brian Moses

Spooky Schools   0 330 41358 9   £3.99
Poems Chosen by Brian Moses

All Pan Macmillan titles can be ordered from our website, www.panmacmillan.com, or from your local bookshop and are also available by post from:

**Bookpost
PO Box 29, Douglas, Isle of Man IM99 1BQ**

Credit cards accepted. For details:
Telephone: +44(0)1624 677237
Fax: +44(0)1624 670923
Email: bookshop@enterprise.net
www.bookpost.co.uk

Free postage and packing in the UK.